UNIT 8
Data Sense

S0-AXK-550

INTER·
Active

Mathematics

Activities & Investigations

GLENCOE
Macmillan/McGraw-Hill

New York, New York   Columbus, Ohio   Mission Hills, California   Peoria, Illinois

Copyright ©1995 by the Glencoe Division of Macmillan/McGraw-Hill Publishing Company.

All rights reserved. Printed in the United States of America. Except as permitted under the United States Copyrights Act of 1976, no part of this publication may be reproduced or distributed in any form or by any means, or stored in a database or retrieval system, without prior written permission of the publisher.

Permission is granted to reproduce the blackline masters contained herein on the condition that such material be reproduced only for classroom use; be provided to students, teachers, and families without charge; and be used solely in conjunction with *Interactive Mathematics: Activities and Investigations.* Any other reproduction, for use or sale, is prohibited without prior written permission of the publisher.

Send all inquiries to:
Glencoe Division, Macmillan/McGraw-Hill
936 Eastwind Drive
Westerville, OH 43081

ISBN: 0-02-824528-8 (Student Resource Book)
ISBN: 0-02-824510-5 (Teacher's Edition)

1 2 3 4 5 6 7 8 9 10 VH 01 00 99 98 97 96 95 94

CONTENTS

UNIT 8 DATA Sense
STATISTICS AND DATA ANALYSIS

Interdisciplinary Applications

DAVID FOSTER

"The national goal is to develop mathematical power for all students. My vision for learning mathematics includes a student-oriented classroom culture, where students are taking charge of their own learning and are actively engaged in a curriculum that reflects today's world, not the mathematics of 150 years ago."

Former Teaching Consultant
  Middle Grades Mathematics
  Renaissance
Morgan Hill, California
Author of Units 1, 2, 5, 6, 7, 8, 10, 11, 13, 15, 16, 17, and 18

David Foster received his B.A. in mathematics from San Diego State University and has taken graduate courses in computer science at San Jose State University. He has taught mathematics and computer science for nineteen years at the middle school, high school, and college level. Mr. Foster is a founding member of the California Mathematics Project Advisory Committee and was Co-Director of the Santa Clara Valley Mathematics Project. Most recently, he has taken the position of Consulting Author for Glencoe Publishing. Mr. Foster is a member of many professional organizations including the National Council of Teachers of Mathematics and regularly conducts in-service workshops for teachers. He is also the author of a book on computer science.

SANDIE GILLIAM

"Many students only see mathematics as isolated number facts and formulas to memorize. By using this program, which incorporates the mathematics into a context of large, real-life units tied together with literature, science, and history, the middle school student can find meaning in the mathematics."

Mathematics Teacher
San Lorenzo Valley High School
Felton, California
Co-author of Unit 14

Sandie Gilliam received her B.A. from San Jose State University and is a mentor teacher and instructor for the Monterey Bay Area Mathematics Project. She was a semi-finalist for the Presidential Award for Excellence in the Teaching of Mathematics in the state of California. Ms. Gilliam has served as a consultant for the California Department of Education and many local school districts and county offices of education. She is a member of the National Council of Teachers of Mathematics and is a frequent speaker at conferences and teacher in-service workshops. Ms. Gilliam was a writer and consultant for Glencoe's *Investigating Mathematics: An Interactive Approach.*

JACK PRICE

"This program is designed to help students become mathematically powerful as they develop problem-solving skills and self-reliance, as well as the ability to work well with others. At the same time, they will strengthen their basic skills and be exposed to new and exciting ideas in mathematics."

Co-Director, Center for Science
  and Mathematics Education
California State Polytechnic
  University
Pomona, California
Author of Unit 3

Jack Price received his B.A. from Eastern Michigan University and his Doctorate in Mathematics Education from Wayne State University. Dr. Price has been active in mathematics education for over 40 years, 38 of those years at grades K through 12. In his current position, he teaches mathematics and methods courses for preservice teachers and consults with school districts on curriculum change. He is president of the National Council of Teachers of Mathematics, is a frequent speaker at professional conferences, conducts many teacher in-service workshops, and is an author of numerous mathematics instructional materials.

KAY McCLAIN

"Building conceptual understanding in mathematics challenges us to re-define what it means to know and do mathematics. This program was developed to allow teachers to become facilitators of learning while students explore and investigate mathematics — strengthening their understanding and stimulating interest."

Kay McClain

Doctoral Candidate
George Peabody College
Vanderbilt University
Nashville, Tennessee
Author of Unit 9, Co-author of Unit 14

BARNEY MARTINEZ

"Students learn mathematics best when their teacher enables them to become actively involved in worthwhile mathematical investigations. Students should be encouraged to interact with each other. Then, through their collaborative efforts, students build their own understanding of mathematics."

Barney Martinez

Mathematics Teacher
Jefferson High School
Daly City, California
Co-Author of Unit 12

LINDA DRITSAS

"This program is designed to encourage students to be creative and inventive, while gaining mathematical power. Open-ended situations and investigations provide the setting that allows students to work at varying depths, while nurturing their natural curiosity to learn."

Linda Dritsas

Mathematics Coordinator
Fresno Unified School District
Fresno, California
Author of Unit 4, Co-author of Unit 12

Kay McClain received her B.A. from Auburn University and her Educational Specialist degree from the University of Montevallo in Montevallo, Alabama. While a teacher at Mountain Brook Middle School in Birmingham, she received the Presidential Award for Excellence in the Teaching of Mathematics in the state of Alabama. Ms. McClain is a Woodrow Wilson fellow and a member of the National Council of Teachers of Mathematics. She regularly conducts teacher in-service workshops and is a frequent speaker at local, state, and national mathematics education conferences. She is also an author of middle school mathematics instructional materials.

Barney Martinez received his B.S. in mathematics from The University of San Francisco and is an instructor of pre-service mathematics teachers at the College of Notre Dame in Belmont, California. Mr. Martinez currently serves on the Mathematics Development Team of the California Department of Education and the Pursuing Excellence Revision Advisory Committee. He is a member of the National Council of Teachers of Mathematics and is very active as a speaker and workshop leader at professional development conferences.

Linda Dritsas received her B.A. and M.A. from California State University at Fresno. She taught middle school mathematics for many years and, for two years, taught mathematics at California State University at Fresno. Ms. Dritsas has been the Central Section President of the California Mathematics Council and is a member of the National Council of Teachers of Mathematics and the Association for Supervision and Curriculum Development. She frequently conducts mathematics teacher in-service workshops and is an author of numerous mathematics instructional materials, including those for middle school students and teachers.

CONTRIBUTORS INTERACTIVE MATHEMATICS

Each of the Consultants read all 18 units while each Reviewer read one unit. The Consultants and Reviewers gave suggestions for improving the Student Resource Books, Teacher's Editions, Cooperative Group Cards, Posters, and Transparencies. The Writers wrote the Student Diversity Strategies that appear in the Teacher's Edition.

CONSULTANTS

Dr. Judith Jacobs, *Units 1-18*
Director, Center for Science and Mathematics Education
California State Polytechnic University
Pomona, California

Dr. Cleo M. Meek, *Units 1-18*
Mathematics Consultant, Retired
North Carolina Dept. of Public Instruction
Raleigh, North Carolina

Beatrice Moore-Harris,
Units 1-18
College Board Equity 2000 Site Coordinator
Fort Worth Independent School District
Fort Worth, Texas

Deborah J. Murphy, *Units 1-18*
Mathematics Teacher
Killingsworth Jr. High School, ABC Unified School District
Cerritos, California

Javier Solorzano, *Units 1-18*
Mathematics Teacher
South El Monte High School
South El Monte, California

WRITERS

Student Diversity Teacher's Edition

Dr. Gilbert J. Cuevas
Professor of Mathematics Education
University of Miami
Coral Gables, Florida

Sally C. Mayberry, *Ed.D.*
Assistant Professor Mathematics/Science Education
St. Thomas University
Miami, Florida

REVIEWERS

John W. Anson, *Unit 11*
Mathematics Teacher
Arroyo Seco Junior High School
Valencia, California

Laura Beckwith, *Unit 13*
Mathematics Department Chairperson
William James Middle School
Fort Worth, Texas

Betsy C. Blume, *Unit 6*
Vice Principal/ Director of Curriculum
Valleyview Middle School
Denville, New Jersey

James F. Bohan, *Unit 11*
Mathematics K-12 Program Coordinator
Manheim Township School District
Lancaster, Pennsylvania

Dr. Carol Fry Bohlin, *Unit 14*
Director, San Joaquin Valley Mathematics Project
Associate Professor, Mathematics Education
California State University, Fresno
Fresno, California

David S. Bradley, *Unit 9*
Mathematics Teacher/Department Chairperson
Jefferson Jr. High
Kearns, Utah

Dr. Diane Briars, *Unit 9*
Mathematics Specialist
Pittsburgh City Schools
Pittsburgh, Pennsylvania

INTERACTIVE MATHEMATICS CONTRIBUTORS

Jackie Britton, *Unit 18*
Mathematics Teacher
V. W. Miller Intermediate
Pasadena, Texas

Sybil Y. Brown, *Unit 8*
Mathematics Teacher
Franklin Alternative Middle
School
Columbus, Ohio

Blanche Smith Brownley, *Unit 18*
Supervising Director of
Mathematics (Acting)
District of Columbia Public
Schools
Washington, D.C.

Bruce A. Camblin, *Unit 7*
Mathematics Teacher
Weld School District 6
Greeley, Colorado

Cleo Campbell, *Unit 15*
Coordinator of Mathematics,
K-12
Anne Arundel County
Public Schools
Annapolis, Maryland

Savas Carabases, *Unit 13*
Mathematics Supervisor
Camden City School District
Camden City, New Jersey

W. Karla Castello, *Unit 6*
Mathematics Teacher
Yerba Buena High School
San Jose, California

Diane M. Chase, *Unit 16*
Mathematics Teacher/
Department Chairperson
Pacific Jr. High School
Vancouver, Washington

Dr. Phyllis Zweig Chinn, *Unit 9*
Professor of Mathematics
Humboldt State University
Arcata, California

Nancy W. Crowther, *Unit 17*
Mathematics Teacher
Sandy Springs Middle School
Atlanta, Georgia

Regina F. Cullen, *Unit 13*
Supervisor of Mathematics
West Essex Regional Schools
North Caldwell, New Jersey

Sara J. Danielson, *Unit 17*
Mathematics Teacher
Albany Middle School
Albany, California

Lorna Denman, *Unit 10*
Mathematics Teacher
Sunny Brae Middle School
Arcata, California

Richard F. Dube, *Unit 4*
Mathematics Supervisor
Taunton High School
Taunton, Massachusetts

Mary J. Dubsky, *Unit 1*
Mathematics Curriculum
Specialist
Baltimore City Public Schools
Baltimore, Maryland

Dr. Leo Edwards, *Unit 5*
Director, Mathematics/
Science Education Center
Fayetteville State University
Fayetteville, North Carolina

Connie Fairbanks, *Unit 7*
Mathematics Teacher
South Whittier Intermediate
School
Whittier, California

Ana Marina C. Gomezgil, *Unit 15*
District Translator/Interpreter
Sweetwater Union
High School District
Chula Vista, California

Sandy R. Guerra, *Unit 9*
Mathematics Teacher
Harry H. Rogers Middle
School
San Antonio, Texas

Rick Hall, *Unit 4*
Curriculum Coordinator
San Bernardino County
Superintendent of Schools
San Bernardino, California

Carolyn Hansen, *Unit 14*
Instructional Specialist
Williamsville Central Schools
Williamsville, New York

Jenny Hembree, *Unit 8*
Mathematics Teacher
Shelby Co. East Middle
School
Shelbyville, Kentucky

Susan Hertz, *Unit 16*
Mathematics Teacher
Paul Revere Middle School
Houston, Texas

Janet L. Hollister, *Unit 5*
Mathematics Teacher
LaCumbre Middle School
Santa Barbara, California

Dorothy Nachtigall Hren, *Unit 12*
Mathematics Teacher/
Department Chairperson
Northside Middle School
Norfolk, Virginia

Grace Hutchings, *Unit 3*
Mathematics Teacher
Parkman Middle School
Woodland Hills, California

Lyle D. Jensen, *Unit 18*
Mathematics Teacher
Albright Middle School
Villa Park, Illinois

Robert R. Jones, *Unit 7*
Chief Consultant,
Mathematics, Retired
North Carolina Department
of Public Instruction
Raleigh, North Carolina

Mary Kay Karl, *Unit 3*
Mathematics Coordinator
Community Consolidated
School District 54
Schaumburg, Illinois

Janet King, *Unit 14*
Mathematics Teacher
North Gulfport Junior High
Gulfport, Mississippi

Franca Koeller, *Unit 17*
Mathematics Mentor Teacher
Arroyo Seco Junior High
School
Valencia, California

Louis La Mastro, *Unit 2*
Mathematics/Computer
Science Teacher
North Bergen High School
North Bergen, New Jersey

Patrick Lamberti, *Unit 6*
Supervisor of Mathematics
Toms River Schools
Toms River, New Jersey

Dr. Betty Larkin, *Unit 14*
Mathematics Coordinator
K - 12
Lee County School District
Fort Myers, Florida

Ann Lawrence, *Unit 1*
Mathematics
Teacher/Department
Coordinator
Mountain Brook Jr. High
School
Mountain Brook, Alabama

Catherine Louise Marascalco,
Unit 3
Mathematics Teacher
Southaven Elementary
School
Southaven, Mississippi

Dr. Hannah Masterson, *Unit 10*
Mathematics Specialist
Suffolk Board of
Cooperative Education
Dix Hills, New York

Betty Monroe Nelson, *Unit 8*
Mathematics Teacher
Blackburn Middle School
Jackson, Mississippi

Dale R. Oliver, *Unit 2*
Assistant Professor of
Mathematics
Humboldt State University
Arcata, California

Carol A. Pudlin, *Unit 4*
Mathematics Teacher/
Consultant
Griffiths Middle School
Downey, California

Diane Duggento Sawyer,
Unit 15
Mathematics Chairperson
Exeter Area Junior High
Exeter, New Hampshire

Donald W. Scheuer, Jr., *Unit 12*
Mathematics Department
Chairperson
Abington Junior High
Abington, Pennsylvania

Linda S. Shippey, *Unit 8*
Mathematics Teacher
Bondy Intermediate School
Pasadena, Texas

Barbara Smith, *Unit 1*
Mathematics Supervisor,
K-12
Unionville-Chadds Ford
School District
Kennett Square, Pennsylvania

Stephanie Z. Smith, *Unit 14*
Project Assistant
University of Wisconsin-
Madison
Madison, Wisconsin

Dora M. Swart, *Unit 11*
Mathematics Teacher
W. F. West High School
Chehalis, Washington

Ciro J. Tacinelli, Sr., *Unit 8*
Curriculum Director:
Mathematics
Hamden Public Schools
Hamden, Connecticut

Kathy L. Terwelp, *Unit 12*
K-8 Mathematics Supervisor
Summit Public Schools
Summit, New Jersey

Marty Terzieff, *Unit 18*
Secondary Math Curriculum
Chairperson
Mead Junior High School
Mead, Washington

Linda L. Walker, *Unit 18*
Mathematics Teacher
Cobb Middle School
Tallahassee, Florida

D A T A
SENSE

Looking Ahead

In this unit, you will see how mathematics can be used to answer questions about statistics. You will experience:

▶ representing information using stem-and-leaf plots, frequency tables, histograms, and line plots

▶ measures of center

▶ reading and interpreting bar graphs

▶ making a histogram from data you create in a simulation

▶ recognizing misleading graphs and statistics

Did You Ever Wonder?

What do mathematics and Balzac Balloon Balls have to do with each other? Turn the page and see how Mary A. Rodas of New York City, combined the two!

Teens in the News

Featuring: Mary A. Rodas
Age: 16
Hometown: New York, New York
Career Goal: Politician or Psychiatrist
Interests: yearbook staff, drama

Mary A. Rodas has been telling CATCO Toys what kids like and what kids will buy since she was 14 years old! Now Mary is 16 and Vice President of Marketing for CATCO Inc., a toy company in New York!

Mary has a real knack for making toys fun. In 1989, CATCO was getting ready to come out with the Balzac Balloon Ball. Mary thought it was a great idea, but suggested they add neon graphics to the package and redo the TV commercial to emphasize the balloon inside the ball. Mary is given credit for the $7 million of Balzac Balloon Balls that have been sold worldwide!

Mary has also helped CATCO with two other new products. Deco Discs are cardboard puzzles that you bend and a CD pops out. She also gave advice on a washable slime that you can eat!

Kids who help test CATCO's products aren't afraid to tell Mary what they really think. Mary uses their input to improve the toys and to decide how to price the toys.

Mary has appeared on the Arsenio Hall Show, The Today Show, Good Morning America, and the Dennis Miller Show. She rides from school to work in a limousine. Mary earns a salary and has stock in CATCO Inc. But she has dreams just like any other teen. Mary is saving her money for college. She hopes to become a psychiatrist or a politician.

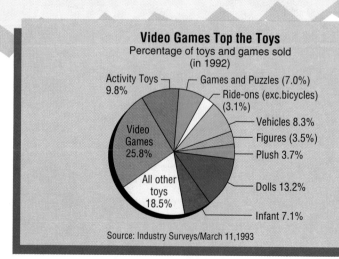

Video Games Top the Toys
Percentage of toys and games sold
(in 1992)

Activity Toys 9.8%
Games and Puzzles (7.0%)
Ride-ons (exc.bicycles) (3.1%)
Video Games 25.8%
Vehicles 8.3%
Figures (3.5%)
Plush 3.7%
All other toys 18.5%
Dolls 13.2%
Infant 7.1%

Source: Industry Surveys/March 11,1993

Team Project

Why Buy?

Marketers like Mary Rodas make better decisions when they have good information. A survey is one way to gather information.

You are a marketer for a company that specializes in products for teens. Your company wants to help them to determine how the students at your school spend their money. What questions will you ask? Decide how many students you will survey. Develop the survey and obtain your data. Use a chart or graph to show the results of your survey. What do you suggest for new products at your company?

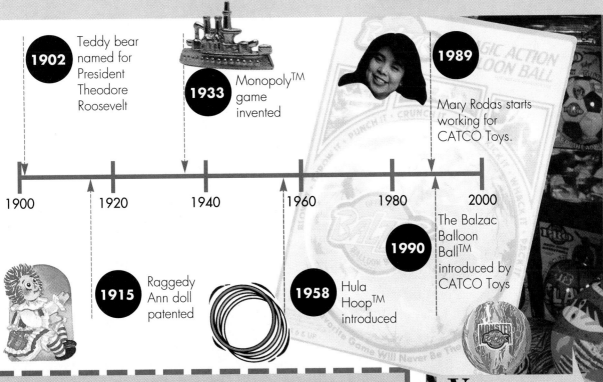

1902 Teddy bear named for President Theodore Roosevelt

1933 Monopoly™ game invented

1989 Mary Rodas starts working for CATCO Toys.

1915 Raggedy Ann doll patented

1958 Hula Hoop™ introduced

1990 The Balzac Balloon Ball™ introduced by CATCO Toys

1900   1920   1940   1960   1980   2000

For more information

If you would like more information about developing new toys, contact:

CATCO Inc.
529 West 42nd Street
New York, New York 10036

You can learn more about the math Mary uses in her job by completing the following activities in this unit.

Setting the Scene

MATHEMATICS TOOLKIT

Many professions require the use of tools. This Mathematics Toolkit includes tools you may find useful during the Data Sense unit. At times you may feel lost or not know where to begin when presented with a problem situation. You should take time to review this toolkit and remember the different statistical tools and problem-solving strategies used by the characters in the following script. You don't need to wait until your teacher tells you to make a chart or find the mean. Instead, if it seems like it might help, try it.

Narrator: Maria, Tran, Asit and Ruth are on the yearbook staff for Jefferson Middle School. They are discussing ideas for a feature article in their yearbook, *The Optimist*.

Maria: Maybe we should do a feature titled "Who is Best Looking?"

Tran: We'd better be careful. We don't want to hurt anyone's feelings.

Asit: The feature page should be cool...we need to attract sales. Let's have something that will include everyone.

Ruth: I've got it. Let's find out what the average seventh grader looks like. That could be our page..."Are you average?"

Maria: I like it! I bet most of our class has brown eyes...

Asit: But, how do we know for sure?

Ruth: We can take a survey, like we did in social studies.

Tran: OK, but what should we ask about besides the color of eyes?

Narrator: The students came up with the following survey.

Average Seventh Grader at Jefferson Middle School

- How tall are you?
  _____ inches
- How much do you weigh?
  _____ pounds
- What color is your hair?
  1. Black   2. Brown
  3. Blonde   4. Red
- What color are your eyes?
  1. Brown   2. Hazel
  3. Blue   4. Green
- Are you 1. Male or
           2. Female ?

Narrator: After getting permission from the principal, the students gave the survey to all seventh graders during first period. With all the data collected, the students continued their discussion.

Asit: Now that we have all this data, how are we going to figure out what the average seventh grader looks like?

Ruth: Easy, we just count up all the information.

Maria: I don't think it's that easy. We have all these numbers, but what do we do with them?

Tran: Can't we make this easier?

Ruth: Remember when we did sampling with raisins in math class? We counted a small sample and that told us something about the whole box of raisins.

Tran: So how many should we use?

Narrator: They decided on 25 surveys for their sample. They picked them at random by placing all the surveys in a large box and drawing 25 of them out without looking. Below is the data from that sample.

- How tall are you?
  61, 59, 64, 73, 58, 62, 61, 63, 72, 63, 56, 69, 67, 75, 62, 63, 61, 64, 58, 64, 63, 61, 72, 59, 63

- How much do you weigh?
  121, 89, 171, 97, 195, 139, 103, 194, 148, 109, 100, 112, 115, 118, 80, 124, 129, 102, 145, 106, 168, 169, 117, 110, 101

- What color is your hair?
  1. Black 2. Brown 3. Blonde 4. Red
  1, 3, 1, 1, 2, 2, 4, 1, 2, 1, 1, 3, 3, 1, 2, 4, 1, 1, 1, 3, 3, 2, 2, 1, 2

- What color are your eyes?
  1. Brown 2. Hazel 3. Blue 4. Green
  1, 3, 1, 1, 2, 1, 4, 1, 2, 1, 1, 3, 3, 1, 1, 4, 1, 1, 1, 3, 3, 1, 2, 1, 1

- Are you 1. Male or 2. Female?
  1, 2, 1, 1, 2, 2, 2, 1, 2, 1, 1, 2, 2, 1, 2, 2, 1, 1, 1, 2, 2, 2, 2, 1, 2

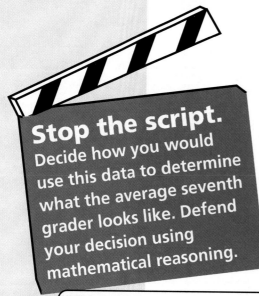

Stop the script.
Decide how you would use this data to determine what the average seventh grader looks like. Defend your decision using mathematical reasoning.

Asit: Let's start with the first question: "How tall are you?"

Tran: I'll make a **stem-and-leaf plot** so we can see what the data looks like. I can use the tens digits as the **stems** and the ones digits as the **leaves**. For example, there are four numbers that have 7 in the tens place. They are 75, 72, 73, and 72. The 5, 2, 3, and 2 are the leaves for the stem 7. So, the number of leaves shows how many values are in each group of ten.

Narrator: Tran creates the stem-and-leaf plot shown below.

tens	ones
5	89698
6	2133349712314143
7	5232

5|8 means 58 inches

Ruth: I don't understand all those numbers all jumbled up like that.

Asit: Well, maybe we can put the leaves in order. Here, I'll do it.

Ruth: Seems right to me. It's what we estimated from the stem-and-leaf plot. Let's analyze the weights now.

Asit: The weights go from 80 to 195 pounds. I think that's going to make a really long stem-and-leaf plot. Maybe we should try a table.

Tran: It looks like we have 25 different weights. A table would be longer than a stem-and-leaf plot!

Maria: We should divide the weights into groups and then tally the weights from the sample.

Narrator: Asit ordered each row of leaves from least to greatest. The result is shown below.

tens	ones
5	68899
6	1111223333344479
7	2235

5|8 means 58 inches

Maria: So... in the first row the numbers are 56, 58, 58, 59, and 59?

Tran: Yeah, you've got the idea.

Ruth: Well, it looks to me like most of this sample is 60-some inches tall. I'd say the average is about 63 or 64 inches.

Asit: But how can we tell for sure?

Maria: How about finding the average? I think it's called the **mean.** You know, you add up all the heights and divide by 25, because we have 25 surveys. Wait, I've got a calculator. The sum of the heights is 1593. 1593 ÷ 25 = *63.72* So the mean height is 63.72 inches.

Ruth: I remember how to make a **frequency table** from math class. First we need to determine a scale for the table. The **scale** must contain all the weights and be separated into equal parts called **intervals.** But before we decide on the intervals, we need to find the **range** of the data by subtracting the lowest weight from the highest weight.

Asit: That would be 195 minus 80. That's 115.

Ruth: The next step is to decide how wide the intervals should be. Interval widths are usually one, ten, one hundred, one thousand, and so on. We should have between 4 and 8 intervals.

Maria: How do we know how many intervals we'll get?

Ruth: We divide the range of the data by the interval width.

Tran: An interval width of 10 means we would need at least 11 intervals.

Ruth: Right, but that's too many intervals.

Asit: How about an interval width of 20? 115 is almost 120 and 120 divided by 20 is 6.

Ruth: Perfect! I'll list the intervals.

Narrator: Ruth makes the following list:
80-99
100-119
120-139
140-159
160-179
180-199

Asit: The scale begins with 80 and ends with 199. That includes all weights in our sample.

Tran: Okay. Let's make the frequency table. Go through the 25 surveys and tally the results.

Narrator: The students make the frequency table shown below.

Interval	Tally	Total
80 - 99	III	3
100 - 119	IIII IIII I	11
120 - 139	IIII	4
140 - 159	II	2
160 - 179	III	3
180 - 199	II	2

Asit: Now that we've created our frequency table, we can use it to create a **histogram.**

Ruth: A histogram?

Maria: It's like a bar graph, only it uses intervals like the ones we used in our frequency table. I'll draw one using the frequency table that we just made.

Narrator: Maria draws the histogram shown below.

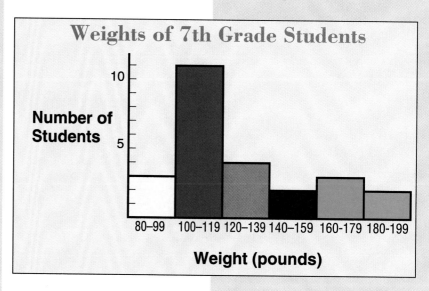

Weights of 7th Grade Students

Number of Students

80–99 100–119 120–139 140–159 160-179 180-199

Weight (pounds)

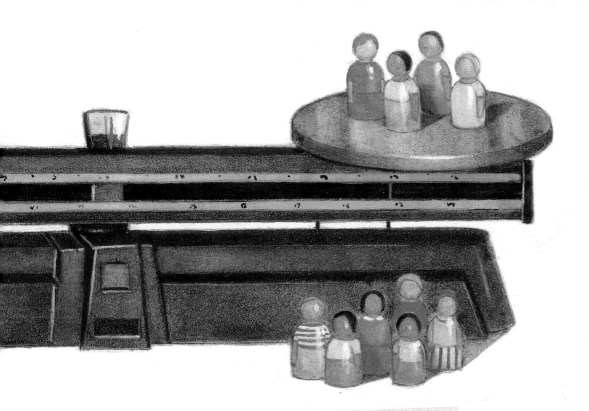

Ruth: Looking at the table and histogram, it looks like the average seventh grader is between 100 -119 pounds, but that range is too big. We need to find only one weight.

Asit: I'll find the mean on the calculator again. The sum of the weights is 3,162. 3,162 ÷ 25 = *126.48* The mean weight is 126.48 pounds.

Tran: 126.48 isn't even in the group with the most people!

Maria: I don't think the mean is right for this data. There are a couple of people who throw the average off. Since the mean weight doesn't even fall in the interval with the most data, maybe we should use the **median**... the weight in the middle.

Tran: Good idea! Let's put the weights in order.
80, 89, 97, 100, 101, 102, 103, 106, 109, 110, 112, 115, 117, 118, 121, 124, 129, 139, 145, 148, 168, 169, 171, 194, 195
Since there are 25 numbers, the 13th number is the middle number. See, it's 117 pounds.

Maria: OK, let's go with 117 pounds as our average weight.

Asit: Next, we have the hair color question. The only numbers we can average are the answer numbers: 1, 2, 3, 4.

Ruth: That doesn't make any sense, especially if we get a fraction answer like $1\frac{1}{5}$.

Maria: Well....what hair color shows up most often? We'll use that as the average.

Narrator: When a value occurs more often than other values in a set of data, we often use that value as an average. That measure is called the **mode**.

Ruth: We should do the same for eye color and the male/female question. I'll make a **line plot** for each of the last three questions.

Narrator: Ruth creates the following line plots.

Hair Color

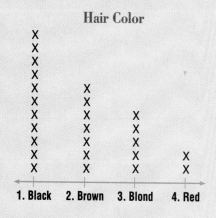

```
X
X
X
X
X    X
X    X
X    X    X
X    X    X
X    X    X
X    X    X    X
X    X    X    X
```
1. Black   2. Brown   3. Blond   4. Red

Eye Color

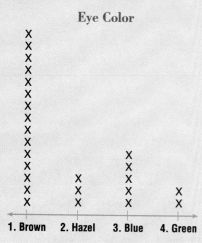

```
X
X
X
X
X
X
X
X
X
X         X
X         X
X    X    X
X    X    X    X
X    X    X    X
```
1. Brown   2. Hazel   3. Blue   4. Green

Gender

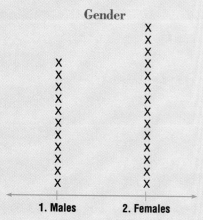

```
          X
          X
          X
     X    X
     X    X
     X    X
     X    X
     X    X
     X    X
     X    X
     X    X
     X    X
```
1. Males   2. Females

Asit: These line plots clearly show that most students have black hair, brown eyes, and are female.

Maria: I think that the black hair and brown eyes are representative of the students, but the difference between the number of males and females is so small that we shouldn't include gender in the traits of our average seventh grade student.

Ruth: I agree, and I don't think we should call this the "average-looking seventh grade student" because most people think that average is always the mean. After all, we only added and divided once to find an average.

Tran: Why don't we change the name to be the "most typical-looking seventh grade student" instead?

Asit: Good idea, but remember this is just a sample of the entire student population. To be really accurate we should evaluate all the data.

Tran: Yeah, we should start that now.

Maria: Wait, before we start I have an idea. We should find all the seventh graders at our school who have all these typical traits, and we can put their pictures on this page.

Ruth: They can be named the "Most Typical Looking Seventh Graders."

Asit: But what about the rest of us?

Tran: We need to show all this data in the yearbook. Remember, it should be interesting to everyone. I know, let's draw graphs of the data on our page. It'll show the entire range of our students.

Maria: We should make histograms from our charts.

Asit: I like it. Now we're all included and we can mark the most typical trait on each graph.

Tran: This is going to be a great page, everyone will want to buy The Optimist this year. We've done a great job!

This concludes the script section of the Mathematics Toolkit. It included many mathematical tools for you to use throughout this unit. As you work through this unit, you should use these tools to help you solve problems. You may want to explain how to use these mathematical tools in your journal. Or you may want to create a toolkit notebook for this purpose.

Mountain Bikes

You are the buyer for a small bike shop. Your decision on which bikes to purchase for the shop is based on knowing how much customers are willing to spend and what the owner can afford to keep in stock. The amount customers will spend on a mountain bike covers a wide range of prices, yet they are all interested in getting the best bike for their money. The owner can afford to carry only three brands of mountain bikes.

You have received a report of tests conducted on the newest models of mountain bikes on the market. Refer to the Mountain Bike Ratings in the Data Bank. Analyze the data and determine which three brands you would recommend that the owner carry. Use mathematical tools and reasoning to defend your recommendations. Be prepared to present your findings to the owner of the bike shop.

THE EXPANSION BRIDGE
Construction Plan Sheet

1. **Construction Plan:** Each crew must submit a construction plan with a construction budget. This plan should detail the way the bridge is to be built, including an explanation of tasks, strategies, construction methods, resource management, and quality checks. Time, cost, and the degree of cooperation are all equally important.

2. **Construction Budget:** Each construction crew should estimate the amount of construction time needed, determine the amount of raw materials required, and total their cost projection. Labor costs are determined at a rate of $1,000 per minute. Raw materials costs are $100.00 per beam and $7.50 per bolt and nut. These amounts make up the budget.

3. **Acquire Raw Materials:** Once a crew submits a budget, the requested raw materials will be delivered to each team. Each crew will want to verify that all of their requested materials are delivered since no raw materials will be delivered during construction. No excess materials may be sold back after construction begins. Additional materials may not be purchased until after the inspection.

4. **Build Bridge:** Each crew begins construction at a given signal. When a construction crew completes the bridge, the finished time is recorded. Specific roles may be assigned but all must participate in the actual construction of the bridge.

5. **Bridge Inspection:** Each bridge is inspected by an independent inspector after all bridges are built. The inspector guarantees that the bridge is constructed in accordance with the company blueprint. All joints must be securely fastened. If a bridge does not meet the standard, a five-minute delay is charged, and the bridge must be adjusted. The total time accumulates while any revisions are made. An additional delivery fee of $500.00 is added to the raw material fee if any additional materials are needed.

The Expansion Bridge Blueprint

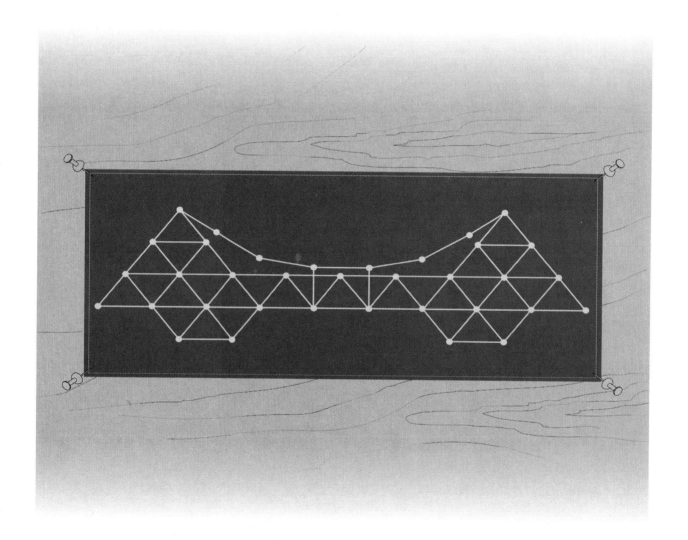

Debriefing Guide

Write a full-page narrative on how your group worked on this expansion bridge simulation. Consider the questions below in writing your narrative. Use them to get started, but don't write only an answer to each question or be limited to just these questions. The narrative will be discussed as a class.

- What methods of construction were considered?
- How did your crew arrive at your estimate?
- Did you follow the plan you developed?
- How was time controlled and quality checked?
- What actions helped/hurt the crew in doing the task?
- How did leadership emerge? Was it shared?
- Were people's individual skills considered?
- Was anyone left out? Were anyone's ideas ignored?
- Was there a sense of satisfaction in building the bridge?
- Would you do anything differently if you could do the construction over again? If so, explain what and why.

THE CONSTRUCTION BID

Below are line plots depicting the construction times, in minutes, of different crews from three different companies. Interpret these line plots. Determine an average construction time for each company to make predictions for future construction jobs. Explain the reasons for your decisions. Make some conjectures (educated guesses) about the construction crews from each company.

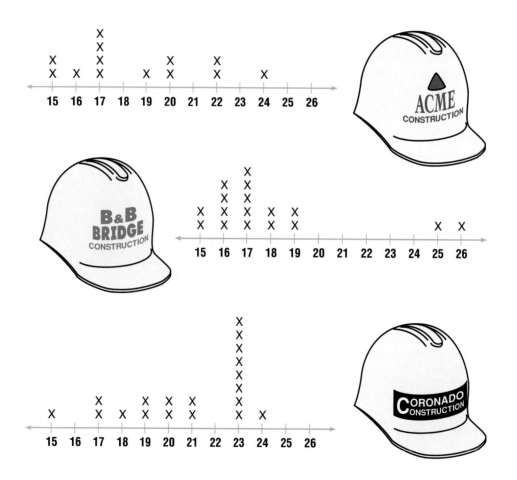

What's the Average?
Mean Median Mode

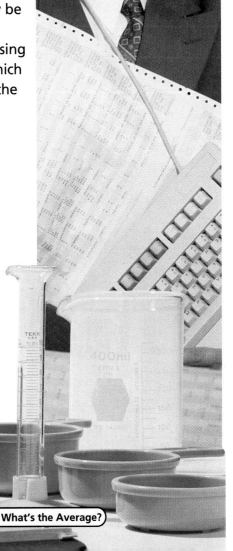

Read all of the Menu Stations. Choose a station. Be sure that each member of your group examines a different situation.

After selecting a station, determine which measure of center you feel best represents the data in the situation given at your station. Write a statement defending your selection with a convincing argument. Explain why the other measures may be irrelevant or even misleading.

Then take turns with other members of your group discussing the situations at the stations in detail. As a group, decide which station you want to present and defend. Another group or the teacher may state a differing opinion for the situation your group presents. Be prepared to defend your choice.

MENU station A

It Must Be The Shoes!

A trendy, new shoe design is out on the market. Depending on how this design sells, the new shoe is a risky investment for a small shoe store owner like Charlie O'Neill. A wholesaler will allow Mr. O'Neill to purchase one size of this new shoe at a reduced price for a special promotion. The following shoe sizes were collected the last time Mr. O'Neill had a special sale.

Shoe Sizes Sold at Last Sale					
8	7	7	9	11	7
$7\frac{1}{2}$	$8\frac{1}{2}$	7	$10\frac{1}{2}$	6	12
8	7	7	10	$10\frac{1}{2}$	9

1 **D**etermine a measure of center that best represents the shoe sizes.

2 **W**rite a statement justifying your choice.

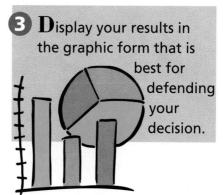

3 **D**isplay your results in the graphic form that is best for defending your decision.

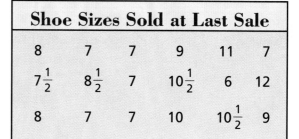

Big Buck$

The vice president of a small company wants to find the "average salary" for the employees of her company. She will use this average salary to make predictions for payroll costs and tax liabilities in preparation for company expansion plans. The payroll manager provided her with the list of salaries below.

$150,000	$90,000	$20,000	$25,000	$90,000	$52,000
$35,000	$90,000	$30,000	$42,000	$42,000	$45,000
$32,000	$20,000	$30,000	$40,000	$25,000	

1 **D**etermine a measure of center that best represents the salaries.

2 **W**rite a statement justifying your choice.

3 **D**isplay your results in the graphic form that is best for defending your decision.

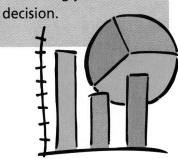

MENU station C

One Size Fits All?

A dress designer for Acme Dress Patterns wants to create a new, unique pattern to use with a revolutionary stretch fabric that has recently become available. This designer believes he can make a lot of money by creating a single pattern that, when used with this new stretchable material, will produce a dress where one size fits all. The pattern should work for all dress sizes with a minimum of stretching or shrinking of the dress. The results of a survey of potential customers are given below.

ACME DRESS PATTERN SIZES

18	12	16	3	6	12
10	6	3	8	10	3
6	8	12	10	3	6
8	8	10	10	6	6

1 **D**etermine the measure of center that best represents the dress sizes.

2 **W**rite a statement justifying your choice.

3 **D**isplay your results in the graphic form that is best for defending your decision.

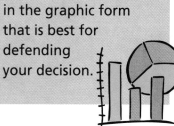

Driving Miss Daily

A traveling sales representative, whose territory is Pennsylvania, sells cable TV subscriptions. After every 60,000 miles she travels, she receives a new company car. What follows are the trip odometer readings she logged during the last 24 days. Estimate how many more days until she is entitled to a new company car.

1 **D**etermine the measure of center that best represents the mileage.

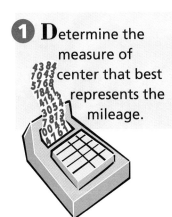

MILEAGE LOG					
180	125	161	39	261	125
310	66	43	89	107	143
96	80	125	10	193	216
178	238	310	170	216	166

2 **W**rite a statement justifying your decision. Then estimate how many more days it will be before she will be entitled to a new company car.

3 **D**isplay your results in the graphic form that is best for defending your decision.

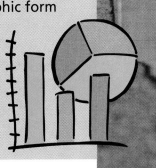

MENU station E

Moving Pay

A big corporation is moving to Silicon Valley in California. A number of employees located on the East Coast will be transferring to this new site in San Jose. The company always gives a housing allowance to transferred executives until they sell their previous home. The housing allowance is calculated at 75% of the "average local home price" in the new location. The vice president of human resources wants to find the average home price and a fair housing allowance. A survey of real estate agencies produced the following list of home prices in neighborhoods near this very expensive housing area.

$625,000	$590,000	$460,000	$790,000	$425,000
$1,050,000	$495,000	$495,000	$740,000	$405,000
$860,000	$580,000	$575,000	$495,000	$550,000

1 **D**etermine the measure of center that best represents the home prices.

2 **W**rite a statement justifying your decision.

3 **D**isplay your results in the graphic form that is best for defending your decision.

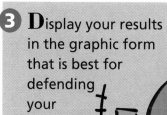

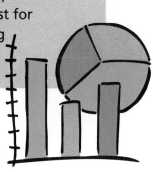

Average News

*T*here are different types of averages. We use these to estimate the center of a set of data. Sometimes the use of one method may give a distorted view of the data.

Look in newspapers or magazines for a real-life example of how one of the averages (measure of center) of a set of data has been determined in order to best understand or use the data. Explain your reasoning. Do you think these measures represent the data in a useful manner?

Super Bowl Scores

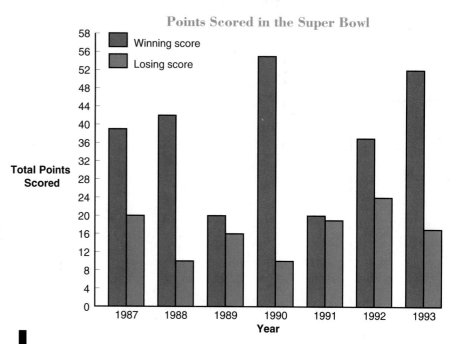

Points Scored in the Super Bowl

Legend:
- Winning score
- Losing score

Y-axis: **Total Points Scored** (0, 4, 8, 12, 16, 20, 24, 28, 32, 36, 40, 44, 48, 52, 56, 58)

X-axis: **Year** (1987, 1988, 1989, 1990, 1991, 1992, 1993)

Interpret the bar graph above. Explain in detail all of the elements of the graph. Include statistical measures. Use mathematics to create additional information from the graph.

Summarize what the graph shows and state any conclusions or trends regarding Super Bowl scores that you have derived from the data generated.

Refer to the "Life in the United States" graphs in the Data Bank or find an example of a bar graph in a newspaper, magazine, or from some other source.

Write a paragraph interpreting the bar graph. Be sure to explain the subject of the graph, each scale, and any conclusions the reader might draw from the graph.

American Railbridges

American Railbridges builds trusses used to support railroad bridges throughout the world. The company is the largest construction company of its kind, but they have a reputation of slow completion times. Below is a histogram that illustrates the amount of time it took construction crews to complete the last 158 trusses.

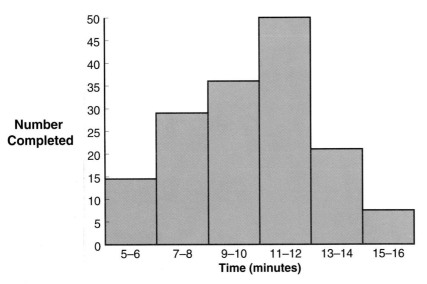

American Railbridges Construction Times

- With your partner, discuss and interpret the histogram above and be ready to share your ideas with the class.
- Describe what the graph might look like if the crews were able to complete the trusses at a much faster rate.

Truss Time

Your class has been hired by the management team of a new competitor to American Railbridges. Your company's first contract is to build at least 30 trusses. You and your classmates have been hired as new construction crews. Below is the blueprint for a truss. Each crew should build these trusses as quickly as possible, insuring quality work. After the completion time is recorded, each crew will disassemble their truss. Then each crew will rebuild a truss to see if they can better their time.

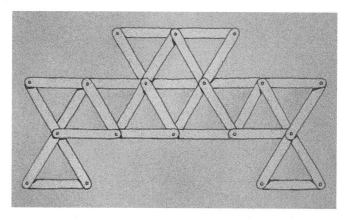

After analyzing the construction times, the management team believes that your company can gain new truss contracts by showing how your crews outperformed the crews from American Railbridges. Using your company's times, design a histogram that will help promote your company to potential customers.

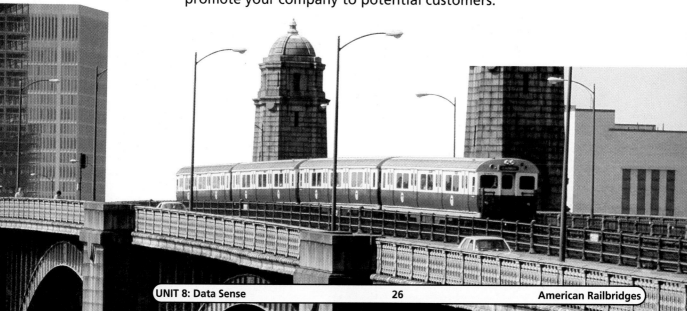

Newark News

Examine and compare the advertisements below.

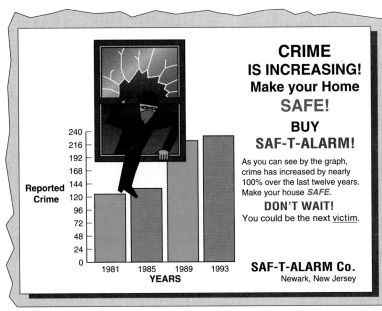

CRIME
IS INCREASING!
Make your Home
SAFE!
BUY
SAF-T-ALARM!

As you can see by the graph, crime has increased by nearly 100% over the last twelve years. Make your house *SAFE.*

DON'T WAIT!
You could be the next <u>victim</u>.

SAF-T-ALARM Co.
Newark, New Jersey

Reported Crime (vertical axis: 0, 24, 48, 72, 96, 120, 144, 168, 192, 216, 240)
YEARS: 1981, 1985, 1989, 1993

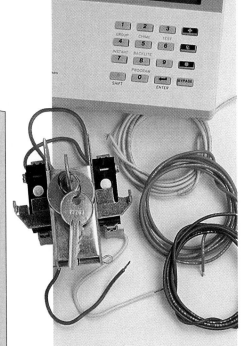

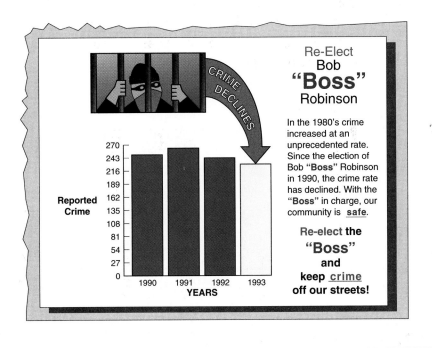

Re-Elect
Bob
"Boss"
Robinson

In the 1980's crime increased at an unprecedented rate. Since the election of Bob **"Boss"** Robinson in 1990, the crime rate has declined. With the **"Boss"** in charge, our community is <u>safe</u>.

Re-elect the
"Boss"
and
keep <u>crime</u>
off our streets!

CRIME DECLINES

Reported Crime (vertical axis: 0, 27, 54, 81, 108, 135, 162, 189, 216, 243, 270)
YEARS: 1990, 1991, 1992, 1993

Both advertisements, *Crime Increases* and *Crime Declines,* appeared in the Newark News, September 24, 1994. They used data from the same source, yet the information presented was very different.

Discuss the advertisements in your group. As a group, submit a letter to the editor explaining how the graphs were drawn to influence the readers and explain how the information was manipulated to make the advertisers' points.

Every Picture Tells a Story

Design a travel brochure describing the temperature a tourist can expect in San Diego during the summer. Be sure to make your brochure attractive to the clients who frequently use your travel agency. Use a histogram and other information to persuade clients to travel to San Diego.

The high temperatures recorded each day in San Diego during the months of July and August, measured in degrees Fahrenheit, are given below.

			79	84	92
	73	76	71	84	95
74	85	72	87	90	91
84	92	88	95	94	88
104	96	92	73	78	82
92	81	72	91	94	96
85	87	86	95	97	76
86	100	98	101	97	103
99	102	100	102	100	98
101	99	100	81	78	77
98	98	89			
99	92				
98					

COMPUTER investigation

Homerun Consultants

You work with a scouting/consulting firm for Major League Baseball. General managers from various teams hire your company to analyze and make recommendations for acquiring new players.

Your company is noted for using statistics to recommend players. You have been the most successful scouting/consulting firm because you use the most modern technology.

A major league team is planning to improve their team next season. Last year, this team was in last place and now needs talent for all positions and in all areas of the game. Both hitters and pitchers are needed to help turn the team around.

Your company has been given the statistics of the forty players who are available. The team requests that your company submit two detailed recommendation reports, one on hitters and the other on pitchers. Break your firm into two pairs, with one pair rating the pitchers and the other rating the hitters.

YOUR REPORT

Each consultant pair should refer to the Baseball Formulas in the Data Bank and write a detailed report, rating the players on their list and giving a statistical argument explaining the players' rating. Graphs, spreadsheet printouts, data lists, and specific information is required in the report along with detailed recommendations and supporting statistical arguments. Each consultant pair will present and defend their findings to the class.

Table Talk

Similar to the mountain bike or baseball player activity, this investigation involves choosing a topic, finding data, and displaying it in a table. After you select a topic and know where or how to find the data, write a statement of need or a problem to solve using the data. For example, remember that

in previous activities the need or problem was to select the top three mountain bikes and to rank the baseball players.

There are many sources of topics and data. Many of these sources are available in libraries. A few suggested sources are periodicals, (*Consumer Reports, Money, Business Week, Newsweek, Sports Illustrated,* and so on), consumer catalogs, almanacs, electronic bulletin boards, or data bases. This data could be consumer products, economic information, sport statistics, or social data. Below are some topic ideas that might get you thinking, but don't feel you need to pick from this list!

What is the best CD player to buy?
Where is the best place to live?
Rank the top ten vacation spots.
Who is the best basketball player ever to play?
Rank the best clothes stores.
What is the typical "family" like?

Select a topic and write a statement describing the need to analyze the data or a problem to solve using the data. Next, organize the data in a table. There must be at least 60 rows in the table.

Select what you feel is the most important criteria for the problem. Interview someone outside of school and ask them which criteria or category is most important to them considering the problem situation.

Analyze the data. Use statistical measures to help rate and compare the data. Determine your findings and conclusions.

Write a detailed report describing your process and conclusions. Make the report persuasive. Use graphs and/or histograms to support your findings.

Write a summary of the process you used in completing this report.

This project is the major assessment for this unit. You may need to do considerable work on this investigation outside of class.

A completed report should include:

- A description of the topic to be analyzed, rated, or ranked.
- A background statement regarding the topic.
- A statement of the need or problem to solve that relates to the topic studied.
- A rationale for choosing the topic.
- A complete list of the data you gathered and the source of the data (minimum of 60 items).
- An explanation of the analysis of the data.
- A description of statistical measures and tools used in analyzing the data.
- A description of the criteria used to analyze the data.
- An interview of someone outside of school on the criteria for analyzing the data.

- All conclusions and findings.
- Statistical graphs depicting the data and supporting your conclusions.
- A summary of the process you used in completing this task.

Selection and Reflection

A student transferred to class near the end of the Data Sense unit. He was assigned to your group and you already know you're going to like working with him. He doesn't have a clue about all the statistical measures and tools you've been using. You offer to help him by listing and describing the statistical measures and tools you've used in the unit. It might help him if you use the tasks in the unit to illustrate your explanation.

In your explanation, you may want to compare the effectiveness of the measures and tools in those situations. What would you say to this student? Write your answer on a separate piece of paper.

Books of the Month

The Problem

Conduct a survey of 20 of your classmates to determine how many books each student read last month. Based on the results of your survey, answer the following questions.

- What is the least number of books read? the greatest number?
- What would the best "average" of the data be? Why?
- Is the data spread out or clustered together? What does this mean?
- If you wanted to use this data to encourage students to read more books, how would you do it? Design a poster or develop a campaign to promote reading.

The Problem

Andrew Cafaro, a professional baseball player, is planning to ask his manager for a raise based on his performance improvements in the past year. Below are his batting statistics for 1993 and 1994.

	1993	1994
Hits	151	144
At Bats	420	396

Should Andrew receive a raise based on these statistics?

Batting a Thousand?

Extension If Andrew is at bat 405 times in 1995, how many hits would he have to make to improve over his 1994 batting average?

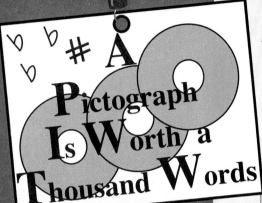

The Problem

A pictograph is a graph that uses pictures or symbols to represent statistical data. The pictographs below are similar to bar graphs, but they use a series of musical notes instead of solid bars to represent the data. Notice that the key tells you that each musical note represents ten units sold.

- Which are more popular: CDs or tapes? How do you know?

- Which type of music is most popular? How do you know?

- Think of three other symbols or pictures you could use to illustrate the data above.

Extension Write some reasons why CDs may be more popular for certain types of music and why tapes may be more popular for other types of music.

The Problem

Nearly eight million American teens do some sort of volunteer work, anything from visiting the elderly to coaching sports to repairing playground equipment. They don't get paid for this work, so why do they do it? The bar graph below gives you an idea.

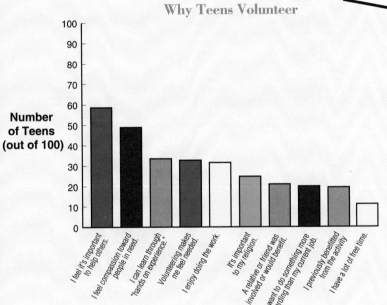

Why Teens Volunteer

Number of Teens (out of 100)

I feel it's important to help others.
I feel compassion toward people in need.
I can learn through "hands on experience."
Volunteering makes me feel needed.
I enjoy doing the work.
It's important to my religion.
A relative or friend was involved or would benefit.
I want to do something more rewarding than my current job.
I previously benefited from the activity
I have a lot of free time.

Teens could choose more than one answer   Source: Independent Sector survey, 1992

- What is the most popular reason why teens volunteer?

- How many teens out of 100 volunteer because they enjoy doing the work? What percent is this?

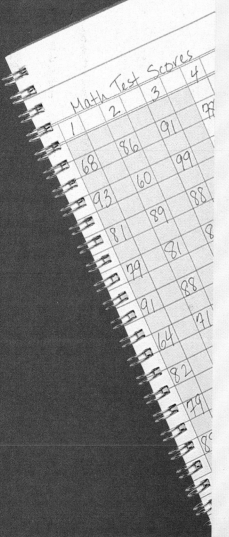

What do you mean?

The Problem

Katrina is taking seventh grade math. Her test scores for the first half of the year are 93, 60, 99, 72, 80, 96, 95, and 91. If Katrina wants to brag about how well she is doing in math, which "average" would she use? Is this average an accurate representation of her grades? Explain.

The Problem

What is your favorite potato chip? A group of professionally trained food tasters came up with the results shown in the chart below. The brands are listed in the order of tastiness.

Which Chip?

- In which category do most of the chips fall?

- Does a higher price necessarily mean a better tasting chip?

- Suppose you are the owner of Albertson's grocery stores. You produce your own brand of potato chips, called Albertson's potato chips. You want to convince people to buy your chips. How could you use the information in the chart and any conclusions based on this information to sell your potato chips?

CHIP PICKS

(The brands are listed in order of tastiness.)

Very Good	Price per ounce
Lady Lee	14¢
Cape Cod	20¢
Jays	18¢
Cape Cod Unsalted	20¢
Eagle Idaho Russet	23¢
Albertsons	12¢
Ruffles	21¢
Lay's Crunch Taters	23¢
Vons	13¢
Good	
Ruffles Light	25¢
Kroger	12¢
Wise	17¢
Charles Chips	21¢
Pringles Original	21¢
Lay's	21¢
Pringles Light Original	24¢
Golden Flake	17¢
Pathmark	10¢
Michael Season's	28¢
Wise Cottage Fries	21¢
Pringles Idaho Rippled Original	22¢
Barrel O'Fun	20¢
New York Deli	24¢
Keebler Ripplin's	19¢
O'Boisie's	25¢
Lay's Unsalted	21¢
Fair	
Munchos	34¢
Keebler Tato Skins	15¢
Poor	
Mr. G's Old-Fashioned	17¢

Source: *Zillions*, June/July 1991

On your feet!

The Problem

Record the number of students in your math class. Then record those who are wearing athletic shoes and what type of athletic shoe they are wearing. Group these by categories such as the ones shown in the diagram below. Next, find out the approximate number of students in your school.

Use your classroom data and the number of students in your school to predict how many students would be wearing each type of athletic shoe.

SNEAKER SEARCH

Here are some of the ways sneakers can differ–

TENNIS: Extra flexibility at ball of foot, extra side-to-side support, reinforced toe.

CROSS-TRAINERS: A combination of features that suits general sports activity, but not serious sports activity.

AEROBICS/FITNESS: Light weight, extra flexibility, light weight sole.

BASKETBALL: Extra side-to-side support, can come in high top versions, rugged soles.

RUNNING: Light weight, extra heel stability, breathable materials.

TABLE OF CONTENTS

Brand and Model: Newest models of mountain bikes.

Price: Manufacturer's suggested retail price

Weight: All tested bikes had a 19- or 20-inch frame.

Shifting ease: How easy it was to change gears while riding. Rated on a five-point scale (1–5) with 5 being the easiest.

Brakes Dry and Wet: How quickly each bicycle went from 15 mph to 0 mph, using both brakes. Rated on a five-point scale (1–5) with 5 being the quickest.

Brake Control: How smoothly the brakes responded. Rated on a five-point scale (1–5) with 5 being the best.

Handling (On-Road and Off-Road): Each bike was tested through a series of maneuvers in both on-road and off-road conditions. Rated on a five-point scale (1–5) with 5 being the best.

Shock Absorption: Each bike was tested by riding it along a 48-foot "ladder" at about 7 mph and judged how severely the bumps were felt through the seat and handlebars. Rated on a five-point scale (1–5) with 5 being the best.

Coasting: Each bike was timed coasting down a steep downhill section of road for one-half mile. Rated on a five-point scale (1–5) with 5 being the best.

Seat Comfort: Men and women testers made this judgment after riding the bikes along a 48-foot ladder. Rated on a five-point scale (1–5) with 5 being the best.

Gear Range: A large range means a more versatile bike. The numbers in this column indicate the number of inches the bike will move with one complete turn of the pedals (in the lowest and highest gear).

Frame Sizes: The smallest and largest frames available. Manufacturers usually make frames in 2-inch increments.

Brand and Model	Price $	Weight lb.	Shifting Ease	Brakes Dry	Brakes Wet	Brake Control
Bianchi Boardwalk	414	29	4	5	3	4
Cannondale SH400	479	28.5	5	4	4	5
Diamond Black	264	33.25	3	5	5	4
Giant Innova	370	27.5	4	4	4	3
Miyata Triple Cross	425	28.75	4	4	3	3
Nishiki Saga 510	510	27.75	5	4	3	5
Peugeot Limestone	350	31.5	4	5	4	4
Raleigh Eclipse CX	262	31	3	4	3	4
Ross Mt. Olympus XC	260	30	3	4	3	2
Schwinn Crisscross	310	29	5	4	2	5
Specialized Crossroads	350	28.5	4	5	2	2
Trek Mult-Track 720	411	30	5	3	3	5
Univega Activa-ES	270	30.5	3	5	3	4

Brand and Model	On-Road Handling	Off-Road Handling	Shock Absrp.	Coasting	Seat Comfort	Gear Range Low/High	Frame Size
Bianchi Boardwalk	3	3	4	4	2	27/108	15.5-23
Cannondale SH400	3	3	1	3	3	25/104	19-25
Diamond Black	2	4	5	2	2	26/89	15.5-22
Giant Innova	4	2	3	2	2	24/96	15.5-23.5
Miyata Triple Cross	2	3	4	5	2	25/100	18-25
Nishiki Saga	3	2	1	5	1	24/96	16-22
Peugeot Limestone	3	3	3	5	5	27/108	18-24
Raleigh Eclipse CX	3	3	3	4	3	27/108	18-24
Ross Mt. Olympus XC	2	3	3	2	2	27/93	19.5-23
Schwinn Crisscross	2	4	4	3	3	27/100	18-22
Specialized Crossroads	3	3	4	3	3	25/100	16.5-22
Trek Mult-Track 720	3	3	3	4	2	25/100	17-23
Univega Activa-ES	2	3	3	3	4	27/93	16.6-22.5

Sports card collectors

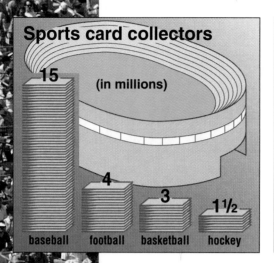

15

(in millions)

4

3

1½

baseball · football · basketball · hockey

Most popular sports

Number of people participating in each sport at least once in 1990 (in millions):

71.4	Exercise walking
67.5	Swimming
55.2	Bike riding
46.2	Camping
41.5	Freshwater fishing
40.1	Bowling
35.3	Exercising with equipment
26.3	Basketball
23.3	Aerobic exercising
23.2	Volleyball

AIDS epidemic

Number of cases reported annually

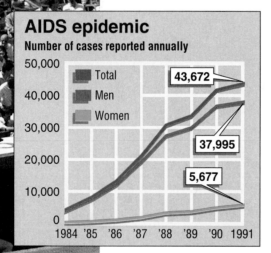

Total
Men
Women

43,672
37,995
5,677

1984 '85 '86 '87 '88 '89 '90 1991

More green thumbs

Percentage of population involved in these lawn and plant activities:

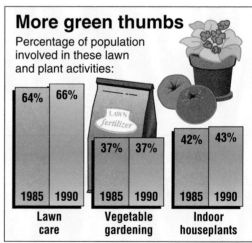

	Lawn care	Vegetable gardening	Indoor houseplants
1985	64%	37%	42%
1990	66%	37%	43%

Scouting rebounds

Number of boys and girls in Boy Scouts and Girl Scouts of America (in millions)

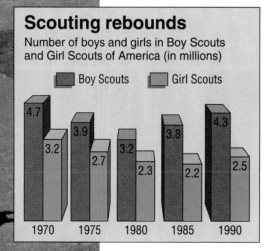

Boy Scouts   Girl Scouts

Year	Boy Scouts	Girl Scouts
1970	4.7	3.2
1975	3.9	2.7
1980	3.2	2.3
1985	3.8	2.2
1990	4.3	2.5

Cable TV explosion

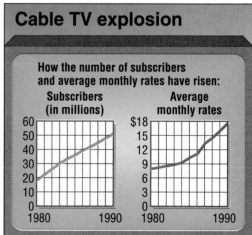

How the number of subscribers and average monthly rates have risen:

Subscribers (in millions)

60 50 40 30 20 10 0
1980   1990

Average monthly rates

$18 15 12 9 6 3 0
1980   1990

BASEBALL FORMULAS

$$AVG = \frac{H}{AB} \qquad ERA = \frac{9 \cdot ER}{IP}$$

$$SLG = \frac{TB}{AB} \qquad PCT = \frac{W}{W + L}$$

$$OB = \frac{H + BB}{AB + BB} \qquad WHIP = \frac{BB + H}{IP}$$

$$KIP = \frac{K}{IP}$$

$$TB = H + 2B + (2 \cdot 3B) + (3 \cdot HR)$$

Hitter's Key

G	games played
AB	times at bat
R	runs scored
H	hits
TB	total bases
2B	doubles
3B	triples
HR	homeruns
RBI	runs batted in
BB	walks (bases on balls)
SB	stolen bases
CS	caught stealing
SO	strikeouts
AVG	batting average
SLG	slugging percentage
OB	on-base percentage

Pitcher's Key

G	games played
IP	innings pitched
H	hits
W	wins
L	losses
R	runs
ER	earned runs
SO	strikeouts
BB	walks (bases on balls)
GS	games started
GF	games finished
CG	complete games
SHO	shut outs
SV	saves
ERA	earned run average
PCT	winning percentage
WHIP	walks-hits ratio
KIP	strikeout ratio

GLOSSARY INDEX

A

Analyze, 12, 32
   data, 31
Approximate, 40
Average, 4, 7, 9, 10, 17, 19, 20,
   21, 22, 23, 34, 35, 38, 44
Average monthly rates, 44

B

Bar graph, 1, 24, 27, 37
Brakes, 42, 43
Budget, 13

C

Calculator, 7, 9
Chart, 4, 11, 39
Coasting, 42
Column, 42
Conjectures, 16 educated
   guesses
Cost, 13, 19
Count, 5

D

Data, 6, 11, 17, 24, 28, 31, 34,
   36, 40
   analysis, 31, 32
   bank, 41-45
   bases, 31
   list, 30
   Sense, 1-45
   set of, 1, 23
Days, 21
Degrees, 29
Digits, 6

E

Estimate, 13, 15, 21, 23
Evaluate, 10

F

Fahrenheit, 29
Feet, 42
Formulas, 45
Frequency table, 1, 7, 8 a
   chart that indicates the
   number of values in each
   interval

G

Gear range, 42
Graphs, 1, 3, 13, 25, 27, 28, 30
   bar graph, 1, 24, 36, 37
   histogram, **8,** 11, 25, 26, 29,
     32
   line plot, **10,** 16
   pictograph, **36**
   stem-and-leaf plot, **6,** 7
   Group, 6, 7

H

Handling, 42
Height, 7
Histogram, 1, 8, 11, 25, 29, 32
   a special kind of bar graph
   that displays the frequency
   of data that has been
   organized into equal
   intervals

I

Inches, 5, 7, 34
Intervals, 7, 8 equal parts on a
   scale
Investment, 18

L

Leaves, 6 in a stem-and-leaf
   plot, the digit(s) in the
   greatest place value(s)
Line plot, 1, 10, 16 a vertical
   graph showing a picture of
   information on a number
   line

M

Mathematics toolkit, 4-11
   problem-solving strategies,
     4
   statistical tools, 4
Mean, 4, 7, 9, 13, 17, 19, 38
   the average
Measures of center, 17, 23
   three common measures
     that help describe a set
     of data; mean, median,
     or mode
   mean, 4, 7, 9, 13, 17, 19, 38
   median, 9, 17, 38
   mode, 9, 17
Measurement
   average monthly rates, 44
   brakes, 42,
   coasting, 42
   cost, 13, 19
   days, 21
   degrees, 29
   feet, 42
   gear range, 42
   handling, 42
   height, 7
   inches, 5, 7
   miles, 41, 42
   miles per hour, 42
   minutes, 13, 25
   month, 34
   odometer reading, 21
   of center, 18, 19, 20, 21, 22
   ounce, 39
   pounds, 5, 8, 9
   price, 42, 43
   rank, 32
   saddle comfort, 42,
   shifting ease, 42, 43
   shock absorption, 42
   size, 18, 20, 42
   temperature, 29
   time, 13, 15, 25
   units, 36
   weight, 5, 6, 7, 8, 9, 42
   years, 2, 24, 27

PHOTO CREDITS

COVER: Jack Holtel,

1, 2, Courtesy Catco,Inc/Mary Rodas; **3**(t), BLT Productions/Brent Turner, (cl), Latent Image, (all others), Courtesy Catco, Inc/Mary Rodas; **4,** BLT Productions/Brent Turner; **5,** Aaron Haupt; **7,** BLT Productions/Brent Turner; **10**(t), Tim Davis/Photo Researchers, (c), Jeffrey Sylvester/FPG, (b), BLT Productions/Brent Turner; **11**(tl), Jonathan Selig/Photo 20-20, (tr), Ed Lettau/FPG, (bl), C. Hamilton/PhotoBank, (r), Aaron Haupt; **12,** Doug Martin; **13,** Tim Courlas; **15,** BLT Productions/Brent Turner; **17,** Life Images; **18,** Doug Martin; **19,** Life Images; **20**(l), Ira Block/The Image Bank, (r), Doug Martin; **21,** Greg Ryan, Sally Beyer/Allstock; **22,** David Barnes/Allstock; **23**(l), Todd Yarrington, (r), Aaron Haupt; **24,** Mitchell B. Raibel/Sports Photo Masters; **25,** Robert Chapek/PhotoBank; **26,** Alain Choisnet/The Image Bank; **27,28,** Aaron Haupt; **29**(l), Courtesy of The Coca-Cola Company, (tr), F. Stuart Westmorland/Allstock, (br), Lawrence Migdale; **30,** Joseph Szkodzinski/The Image Bank; **31,** Dennis Hallinan; **32,** BLT Productions/ Brent Turner; **34,** Jeff Bates Photography; **35,** Jonathan Kirn/Sports Photo Masters; **36**(t), NBC/Shooting Star, (c), Steve Jennings/LGI Photo Agency, (b), Dean Dixon/LGI Photo Agency; **37,** Jeff Bates Photography; **38, 39,** Aaron Haupt Photography; **40,** Doug Martin; **41**(b), K S Studios/Bob Mullenix; **42,43,** Doug Martin; **45,** Brian Stablyk/Allstock, (inset), Aaron Haupt;

ACKNOWLEDGMENTS

39, "The Great Potato Chip-Off." Copyright 1991 by Consumers union of U.S., Inc., Yonkers, NY 10703-1057. Adapted with permission from **ZILLIONS**, June/July 1991. Although this material originally appeared in **ZILLIONS** the selective adaption and resulting conclusions presented are those of the author(s) and are not sanctioned or endorsed in any way by Consumers Union, the publisher of ZILLIONS; **42-43,** "Mountain Bikes." Copyright 1990 by Consumers Union of U.S., Inc., Yonkers, NY 10703-1057. Adapted with permission from **CONSUMERS REPORTS**, November 1990. Although this material originally appeared in **CONSUMER REPORTS**, the selective adaption and resulting conclusions presented are those of the author(s) and are not sanctioned or endorsed in any way by Consumers Union, the publisher of **CONSUMER REPORTS**.

Textbook Adoption Copy
EML, James Madison University
See also other possible titles in this series